MASTER OF THE DEAD

and Other Strange Unsolved Mysteries

MARGARET RONAN

SCHOLASTIC BOOK SERVICES

New York Toronto London Auckland Sydney Tokyo

ISBN 0-590-30005-9

12 11 10 9 8 7 6 5 4 3 2 1   9   9/7 0 1 2 3 4/8

Printed in the U.S.A.   06

CONTENTS

INTRODUCTION

"Where do you get these stories? Did they really happen? Are they true?"

Readers often write to me asking these questions. They deserve to be answered. It's fun to have unsolved mysteries to puzzle over —but it's even more fun if we know the mysteries are based on recorded facts.

Yes, as far as I know, the events in this book really happened. Some I found in old records and reports. Some of them were told to me by eyewitnesses. Some are based on newspaper clippings. The people who recorded or reported the mysteries really believe they happened. However, I am reporting these mysteries secondhand. They did not happen to me.

Some of the names of people and places have been changed by request. Many of the conversations in the stories have had to be recreated. But as far as possible, I have stuck closely to what was told me in interviews, and what was written in black and white in old and new records. It is up to you to decide whether or not you believe the stories in this book.

The world is full of events we can't yet explain logically. But someday, when we know more about the laws that govern our universe, so-called unsolved mysteries may be as easy to understand as radio, television, or space travel is today.

—Margaret Ronan

THE MILL VALLEY MONSTER

In the spring of 1972, the lights came to Mill Valley.

Mrs. Clara Macklin was the first to see them. "I was up early, setting out plants in my garden before the day got too hot," she remembers. "I saw a kind of flash out of the corner of my eye. I turned around, and there were these three bars of clear white light moving across the road right in front of my house. When they got to this side, they moved right up my picket fence — almost as if they knew what they were doing. If I try to describe them, the nearest I can come is to say they were something like neon tubes, sort of solid and glowing. Then I heard a loud pop and they were gone. There were scorch marks on the fence."

As soon as Mrs. Macklin could catch her breath, she screamed. The noise brought her husband and neighbors out of their homes. She pointed out the scorch marks and gasped out her story. Then everyone hunted for an explanation — which was hard to find. There had been no traffic on the road. There were no glass windows across the way to cause odd reflections. In fact there was nothing across the road but an empty field with trees at the far side.

"Maybe some kid was playing tricks with a mirror from behind the trees," said a neighbor.

"Looks more like tricks with a blowtorch," said another.

Mrs. Macklin only shook her head. These lame explanations didn't account for the bars of light that seemed so solid. Besides, although she didn't say so at the time, the lights seemed to her to have a kind of *intelligence*. "I know it sounds crazy," she recalls, "but I got the impression that they were looking over the neighborhood."

Two days later there was another strange visitation. Mr. Macklin was reading his paper in the living room in the early afternoon. Suddenly he called out, "Clara, come look at this thing!"

Mrs. Macklin hurried in from the kitchen. Her husband was sitting bolt upright, his eyes fixed on the further wall. He pointed mutely at a spot just behind her head.

Clara Macklin swung around, and gasped.

Suspended in mid-air, between her and the wall, was a blob of glowing, ruby-colored light.

As the Macklins watched in stunned silence, the blob rose to within a foot of the ceiling. Then it began to move about the room as if investigating every corner and cranny. By then the Macklins had recovered enough to notice that wherever the light went, the room seemed to darken. "Sunlight was pouring in, yet wherever the red light went, it got shadowy. Then all of a sudden there was a loud pop, and the red light was gone. In a few seconds the room was sunny again."

In an effort to solve the mystery, Mrs. Macklin got in touch with a friend who taught physics at a nearby high school. "He told me about ball lightning — some kind of electrical discharge, which has been known to bounce in and out of houses. But what he described didn't sound like what we had seen. Besides, there had been no thunderstorms in the area for more than a week."

Puzzled and uneasy, the Macklins decided to say nothing about their latest experience to their neighbors. But they got some unexpected backup. Pat Borne, the man who lived in a small one-story house to the right of them, knocked on their door the next morning.

His visit came as a surprise. Borne had hardly exchanged five sentences with the Macklins in the five years that they had been neighbors. He had not even left his house the morning when Mrs. Macklin first encountered

3

the white lights. Instead he had watched from his window with disapproval as the other neighbors gathered around her. Yet now here he was at the Macklin door with an apologetic look on his face.

"I was pretty rude the other morning," he admitted. "But I think now we're all in the same boat. I had an experience last night that I think you folks might be interested in."

Borne had gone to bed late, after carefully locking up. Unable to sleep, he switched on the small TV set beside his bed. For a time he lay watching an old movie. "Then three bars of white light began cutting across the screen. I figured there was something the matter with the set, and switched it off. But the lights didn't go away. Then I unplugged the set, and the lights crawled right off the screen, up the wall, and out the window. Darndest thing I ever saw."

"What did you do?" asked Mr. Macklin.

"What could I do? It wasn't something you can call the police about, was it? I've got a theory, though. They've got those big fancy machines down at the university, doing all kinds of who knows what kinds of experiments. Maybe they're setting up some crazy electrical field that's gotten out of control. But it's no good asking. Whatever they're doing is probably top secret."

"Maybe you're right," Macklin agreed. "But thanks anyway for telling us about it. Clara and I were beginning to think we were seeing things."

4

Mr. Macklin needn't have worried. In the week that followed, a lot of other people nearby also began to see things. In broad daylight, a large pinkish ball of light rolled back and forth across the roof of the house at the end of the road before vanishing with a loud pop! Several bars of white light, which seemed to be linked together, interrupted a barbecue in the Gordons' back yard. And then there was the weird appearance in the Bayliss house.

"I was giving the children lunch," Mrs. Bayliss recalls. "A blob of red light suddenly formed over the table. It kept contracting, then expanding — almost as if it was breathing. The children thought it was a joke — they're too little to be scared. I'll admit that I was terrified. You see, there was this kind of blackness growing around the light — like a hole in the air. Of course, that was just an impression I got. . . ."

Because his wife was so upset, Jim Bayliss called the local electric power company. They sent inspectors, followed by workmen who checked out power lines, electrical wiring, and even electrical appliances.

The investigation by the power company came up zero. But Mr. Bayliss kept on trying. Next he consulted weather experts at the university for information on possible storms in the area. There had been none at the time of the lights. But even Bayliss drew the line at calling the police. The lights just didn't seem to be a police matter.

Almost as if the lights knew they were being checked out, they withdrew — for six peaceful weeks. Then, in late May, they made their last appearance. It was a grand finale!

"We had been painting the front room all day, and we were dead tired," says Mrs. Macklin. "We went to bed early, and both of us fell into a deep sleep.

"You have to realize that it was a hot, sultry night. We don't have an air conditioner — my husband says they're bad for his sinuses. But it was a feeling of cold that woke me. My feet were freezing.

"I sat up in bed to pull the cover up. Right across the foot of the bed there was this blob of red light. I grabbed my husband and shook him awake.

"The cold seemed to be coming from the blob. Our teeth were chattering, but neither of us could make a sound. Then the blob started to roll up the bed toward me. I remember thinking, 'If it touches me, I'll die!' But it suddenly veered off the side of the bed. I thought it was probably on the floor, but I didn't dare look."

All at once the side of the bed on which Mrs. Macklin lay tilted sharply over, almost throwing her out. She screamed and grabbed the headboard. Now she could see the floor, but she couldn't believe her eyes.

The blob of light was vanishing into the floor. Around it a large black stain seemed to be spreading beside the bed. But it wasn't a stain. A huge black hole was opening, and the bed was tipping into it.

Mrs. Macklin remembers her husband jumping out of the other side of the bed and dragging her after him. "He pulled me through the window. We were out on the lawn in our nightclothes. The last thing I saw was the bed, hanging over that hole!"

The Macklins ran to Pat Borne's house and pounded on the door. But Borne never came to the door. As it turned out, he wasn't even in the house.

Other neighbors came to the aid of the Macklins, and called the police. But from that night on, Pat Borne was never again seen in the neighborhood.

"He just dropped out of sight," Mrs. Macklin says. "Nobody ever heard of him or from him again. And, you know, the funny thing is that when the police went through his house, there wasn't a sign of a bed in it. What do you suppose he did with his bed? I don't like to think about that too much."

What about the Macklins' own bed? When they got up enough courage to go back into their house that night, there it was! "The police told us we must have had a nightmare, but I guess they thought we had a drink too many," says Mr. Macklin. "Anyway, there wasn't any hole. The floor was all there. But if it was a nightmare, we both had it at the same time — and that's not very likely."

One reporter, who interviewed the Macklins, came up with this theory. He suggested that human beings sometimes store up large amounts of static electricity. Could Pat Borne have been a kind of human storage battery? Was he perhaps the source of the Mill Valley lights?

The Macklins don't think so. "That explanation doesn't answer anything," says Macklin. "It just raises more questions. What about the way the pink blob seemed to eat light? What about that hole in our floor — our bed almost fell into it! God knows what would have happened if we had hung around to see if we were imagining it. But the biggest question is what happened to Pat Borne — and *his* bed?"

THE TIME TREE

Glenn Corwin used to be crazy about trees. He can't stand the sight of them now.

Glenn was born and brought up in the Southwest. Until he was eight, the tallest vegetation he had ever seen was cacti. Then his father took him to Ohio to visit relatives. Glenn couldn't believe the trees there. He thought he had never seen anything so beautiful.

You have to know this to understand the house Glenn built. He was about 40 when his father died and left him some money. Glenn went back to Ohio and bought a piece of land. It was on a rise of ground with a few big old oaks on it. Glenn picked out the biggest oak and told the builder he wanted a house built around it.

"It won't work," said the builder. "This tree's got big roots. If we can work the pipes down among them, the roots will grow through them in time. Besides, how can we make the roof weather-tight with the tree growing up through it?"

"Do the best you can," said Glenn. "Just make sure that tree is in the center of the house. I don't want a branch of it cut off, either."

The builder's "best" turned out to be a kind of A-frame, three-room house, with the tree in the middle of the living room. The trunk went up through the ceiling, and the branches almost concealed the roof from the outside. Glenn liked it a lot. But he only lived in it one month. After June 22, 1948, he never dared enter it again.

The trouble began about a week after Glenn moved in. He was cooking a meal in the kitchen when he heard the noise. It was a high-pitched sound, somewhere between a scream and a piercing whistle.

Thinking that a squirrel might have gotten trapped between the roof and the tree, he ran into the room. Slats had been nailed on the tree to form a kind of ladder, and he climbed up them to have a look at the ceiling.

When he was almost at the top of the ladder, the noise seemed to drop below him, rising and falling as if it came from a moving object. Puzzled, Glenn climbed back down. As he reached the midway point of the tree, the whistling scream seemed to intensify. He felt as though it was piercing his skull.

In self-defense, he clapped his hands over his ears. As he did so, there was a loud cracking sound, followed by a sharp bang. Then there was silence.

Dazed, Glenn stared around him. Slowly, he took his hands away from his ears. Everything was quiet. He and the tree were the only living things in the room.

Not surprisingly, he didn't sleep well that night. He kept waking out of nightmares in which a crowd of men moved restlessly about, muttering and cursing. Sometimes they stopped and looked upward expectantly. When they did, he became afraid.

The sound of knocking on his door brought him out of a heavy doze the next morning. Groggily, he pulled on a robe, and went to see who was there. The man who stood outside was tall and thin. His sunburned face was heavily lined, but the eyes were surprisingly youthful and bright.

"I'm Jamie Dodd," he said with a grin. "I'm your nearest neighbor. Got a little farm about two miles down the road. I could drop off eggs, butter, and vegetables a couple of times a week, if you're interested. You could probably use the food, and I could use the extra money."

Glenn thought he had never been so glad to

see another human being. "Thank you, I'd be glad to do business with you. Come on in and join me in some coffee," he said eagerly.

"Don't mind if I do," Dodd admitted. "There's a lot of talk hereabouts on the way you had this place built — putting it up around a tree and all. The truth is, Mr. Corwin, you could probably sell tickets. Everybody's mighty curious."

"No need to buy tickets," Glenn laughed. "Anybody in the area is welcome to come and see for themselves. I'd be glad of the company. Now, why don't you step in and let me show you around."

The tree seemed to hold a special fascination for Dodd. He walked slowly around it, then stood looking up at it. "This tree's been here a long time," he said finally. "It must be 40 — 50 feet high. It's seen a lot of history in these parts. Good thing it can't talk, eh?"

Glenn had been on the point of telling Dodd about his strange experience of the day before. But the farmer's words sent a sudden chill through him and made him change his mind. Later, after Dodd had gone, he was sorry he had kept silent.

During the afternoon, he couldn't get Dodd's words out of his mind. If the tree could talk . . .? Irritated at himself, he got out a ladder and climbed up to the roof outside to check for trapped squirrels. But there was nothing on the roof, only the spread of thick, leafy branches.

He stayed outside doing chores as long as he could. The sun was going down when he finally forced himself to go back into the living room. "You'd better pull yourself together," he told himself. The best way to do that seemed to be to build a fire and settle down in front of it with a book.

He had read for about half an hour when the noise started. A steady creak . . . creak . . . creak. . . . It reminded him of the sound made by a swing in a playground.

He forced himself to be calm. The sound seemed to be coming from about three or four feet above his head. Could it be a branch rubbing against the roof outside? But it was a still, calm evening. There was no wind.

Creak . . . creak . . . creak. . . . "Don't let the screaming start in," he whispered. "Please don't." But he knew it would start. And here it came now, high-pitched and thin, as if it were forced out of some narrow passage. As before, it was followed by the loud cracking sound, then the bang. And then silence.

For a long time Glenn huddled in his chair, staring at the tree. When he finally got to his feet, he was shaking so badly that he could hardly get the front door open. He spent the night sitting on the steps outside.

Jamie Dodd found him there when he came to deliver the vegetables and eggs the next morning.

"You're up early," he called cheerfully. But

he thought Corwin looked like a man who hadn't even been to bed.

Corwin says now that he doesn't remember Dodd's arrival. Dodd claims that Corwin just looked at him blankly and muttered, "Got to tear the whole place down. Wouldn't want anybody to buy it. It's got some kind of curse on it."

Corwin left Ohio two weeks later. Dodd offered to help him pack up his belongings for shipment, but Corwin shook his head. "I can't take anything out of that house," he explained. "It might be tainted."

"You sound like you need a long rest," Dodd told him.

Before leaving, Glenn Corwin talked about having the house torn down. He didn't have to, as it turned out. Vandals broke the windows and smashed in the door. The weather and the roots of the tree finished the place off. The foundations cracked. One night lightning struck the tree, and what remained of the house burned to the ground.

Afterward, Dodd wrote to Corwin. "I'm afraid your house is a total loss," the letter said, "but I don't think you'll mind. Now that it's gone for good, it turns out that maybe you were right about a curse. They found a skeleton under the foundations out at your place. It had a broken piece of rope tied around its neck and a bullet hole in the skull. That struck me as real interesting, so I started checking around in the old files at the newspaper office.

In 1872, a fellow named Jake Turk robbed a bank that used to be right on the edge of your property. The sheriff got the drop on him as he was making his getaway. People were pretty steamed up, so they grabbed Jake and strung him up to that tree you had in your house. But the lynchers were in such a hurry that they didn't do a good job with the noose. Jake kept struggling, and the rope broke. In cases like this, a hanged man who lived to tell about it could generally go free. But while Jake was lying on the ground, some fellow stepped up and shot him. Now I don't know why you took such a dislike to your new house, Mr. Corwin. But with all your talk about curses, I thought you might already have heard about Jake Turk. Maybe it preyed on your mind. But in any case, it wasn't a good idea to build your house the way you did. Trees live a long time. Who's to say that they don't have long memories, too?"

SPRINGHEEL JACK

Like many of his fellow Englishmen, Squire Matthew Cathorn enjoyed a brisk, daily walk. It was his habit to take a stroll every afternoon along the winding lanes near his home in Surrey. On the afternoon of November 18, 1837, it had begun to rain lightly, but the squire didn't mind. He put on an old coat and set off, prepared to enjoy himself. It didn't work out that way.

For about a mile, he met no one. Then suddenly, he heard something moving among the trees behind the six-foot-high wall that flanked the lane. It sounded like a large something.

Squire Cathorn had lived in the country all his life. He knew the sounds made by four-footed animals, and this didn't sound like an animal to him. He quickened his pace. He knew that cities like London were full of thieving rascals who carried cudgels. Perhaps one of them had migrated to his own neighborhood. Perhaps he ought to get home as quickly as possible, and get word to the constable.

What happened next stopped him in mid-stride. A figure hurtled through the air and over the wall, landing on its feet directly in front of the squire. It was a man — tall, thin, and strange-looking. Close-fitting metallic-looking garments covered him from neck to feet. A short cloak spread out around him like wings. On his long, narrow head was a tall metal helmet. When he grinned at the squire, Cathorn noticed the man's teeth were yellow and as pointed as his odd, batlike ears.

The man also had unusually long, bony fingers. With these he reached out and grabbed Cathorn, lifting him off the ground. For a moment he held him there, then flung him on his back. The long bony fingers went busily through the squire's pockets, taking his money and his watch. Then the creature straightened up. He seemed to gather himself together, then leaped straight up in the air. Cathorn stared in astonishment as the man soared over the wall as though the force of gravity didn't exist.

Several minutes passed before Cathorn dared get to his feet. He was badly shaken. As quickly as he could, he hurried off to the cottage where Jack Norton, the district constable, lived.

Did Norton think the old man had lost his mind? Not at all. In fact, Norton wasn't surprised. But he was worried. "I was afraid this might happen sometime," he said. "You've just met Springheel Jack, sir. He's been terrorizing folks up in London. The Lord Mayor has had vigilante committees and horse patrols after him. Even the Duke of Wellington has been riding out with a brace of armed men looking for Springheel. Perhaps it's the Duke who's scared him into our neighborhood, eh?"

By the time Cathorn had met Springheel Jack in the lane, Londoners knew him well. For weeks he had been jumping out at well-to-do citizens in parks, deserted streets, and on lonely commons. He snatched their purses. If they were carrying food, he took that. His ability to leap high into the air had gotten him his nickname. Once, when a group of outraged citizens cornered him, Jack had leaped right over their heads and escaped.

"They say he's got hidden springs in his boots, and that's how he can leap so high," Norton told Cathorn.

"I didn't see any springs," Cathorn replied.

"They also say he's got a kind of pistol that squirts out balls of fire and puts you to sleep. You're lucky if you didn't see that," Norton retorted.

But an 18-year-old girl named Jane Alsop wasn't so lucky.

Jane lived at Bear Bine Cottage in the village of Old Ford. It was an out-of-the-way place, and the news of Springheel Jack hadn't yet reached there. Otherwise, Jane might not have been so quick to answer the knock at her door on the night of February 28, 1838.

Since it was dark outside, Jane carried a lantern. She held it high as she opened the door. Its light was pale compared with the flashing lamp strapped to the chest of the man who stood outside.

"Who is at the door?" Jane's sister Anne called.

Jane's answer was a scream. It was cut short as the long, bony fingers of the man grabbed her throat.

Anne rushed downstairs to see what was the matter. A tall man with pointed ears and strange clothes was grappling with her sister. Anne snatched up a poker from the fireplace and lunged at him. He let go of Jane and pulled out something that looked like a metal pipe. Balls of fire squirted from it into Anne's face, knocking her down. Then the man leaped through the door and was gone.

As he bounded over the garden wall, Jane saw his cloak fall from his shoulders. A second later, a shadowy figure stood up from behind the bushes by the door. It also seemed to be wearing a cape and a pointed helmet. It ran down the path, snatched up the cape, and leaped over the wall.

Although Jane's throat was bruised and

her sister unconscious for several minutes, neither girl was really hurt. Both were badly scared, but able to give a good description of the visitor. It matched the description given by other victims of Springheel Jack. But there was one outstanding difference about the attack at Old Ford. For the first time on record, Jack seemed to have brought along an accomplice.

Jane's experience made newspaper headlines. It also encouraged more people to report encounters with Springheel Jack. Several men said Jack had knocked them down with his fire-spitting weapon and taken their coats and shoes. A baker's boy ran into Jack and lost his tray of bread. And then there was the case of Miss Soules, who lived in the London district known as Limehouse.

It was sundown, and Miss Soules and her sister were threading their way along a narrow lane known as Green Dragon Alley. They had met no one on the way — until a tall, caped figure suddenly bounded in front of them.

Miss Soules thought at first, because of the cape and the tall hat he wore, "that he was a gentleman." But he didn't behave like one. He flung back the cape, and a lantern blazed forth from his chest. Then out came the weapon and the spitting balls of fire.

Miss Soules dropped to the ground unconscious. Her sister screamed the place down. But Springheel Jack was out of sight with their purses before help got to the two women.

Jack made his final London appearance the very next day. He knocked on the door of the London home of a Mrs. Ashworth. But when the servant who opened it started to scream, he went hurriedly away.

Six months later, in July, something happened near Liverpool that might — or might not — have had something to do with the case of Springheel Jack. A police inspector named Hemer was walking near Toxteth Park.

It was a clear night, without a cloud in the sky. So Hemer was surprised and startled when what seemed to be a bright flash of lightning lit up a nearby field.

But it wasn't lightning. It was a huge, circular, glowing shape which hung motionless over the field for several minutes. Then it gave off a thick shower of fiery sparks and began to sink toward the ground. The inspector discovered that he didn't really want to inspect this mystery. He ran away.

Could the glowing object have been a UFO? And if it was, did it have anything to do with Springheel Jack's disappearance from England? After 1838, he was never seen again in that country.

There are people around today who think Springheel Jack was a visitor from outer space. His weird costume, they say, may have hidden an anti-gravity unit that made it possible for him to make gigantic leaps and sail

21

through the air. As for his strange weapon that knocked his victims unconscious, there was certainly no earthly "ray gun" like that in 1838.

If you can go along with this theory, it's easy to imagine Jack as someone on a mission of exploration. Then his behavior makes more sense. Like any explorer, he would collect specimens — clothing, food, money, watches, for example. Perhaps he was trying to collect a human specimen when he came to Jane Alsop's cottage.

But people in 1838 didn't tend to think in terms of aliens from outer space. Some authorities thought Jack was really a true earthling named the Marquis of Waterford.

The Marquis was a wealthy, well-to-do, good-for-nothing whose idea of a joke was to put on a disguise and hold up a village tavern, or set fire to a farmer's haystacks, or carry off a pretty village girl. Since British noblemen in the 19th century were seldom prosecuted for such pranks, and since the Marquis always paid for any damage he did, he got away with it. Being Springheel Jack fitted his idea of fun, but no one could find any real evidence to tie him in with a being who carried a ray gun and leaped over tall walls with a single bound.

The mystery of Springheel Jack has never been solved. And it has an eerie postscript. In 1944, the town of Matoon, Illinois, was terrorized by a strange intruder. He wore silvery, close-fitting garments and a metal helmet. His ears were pointed and he could leap like a kangaroo. For about a month, he popped up to stare in the windows of Matoon homes. When someone looked out, he would point a device at them which squirted fire and knocked them out.

The Matoon police ran around in circles trying to capture him. The Illinois state police put out a dragnet, but it didn't help. As suddenly as he came, the intruder vanished.

Was it possible that he was Springheel Jack, 106 years older but as spry as ever? If that seems too outlandish an idea, how about this one? Imagine a race of Springheel Jacks, still exploring our planet, still on the lookout for interesting specimens.

THE CREEPING
MOLD

You've seen them in science-fiction movies — those creeping spores and deadly growths that swallow up everything that gets in their way. It's fun to watch such goings-on in a film because we know they couldn't happen in real life. Or could they?

The fact is that something very like this kind of creepy movie plot did happen in Surrey County, North Carolina, not too long ago.

The terror had its beginning in a roll of linoleum. Grady Norman was driving past the old dairy house when he saw the linoleum leaning against the building with the "FOR SALE CHEAP" sign on it.

Grady braked to a stop. The man who had been living in the dairy house was moving out.

At the moment he was loading his possessions into a battered truck. Grady pointed to the linoleum.

The man nodded. "Practically brand new. Bought it for my wife, but she got sick and died before I could get it laid down. You can have it for half what I paid."

It was too good a bargain to resist. Grady bought it and took it home. As he had expected, his wife, Daisy, was pleased. She was a good housekeeper, and the linoleum would make her work easier.

She was not so pleased to hear about where he bought the linoleum. "From what I've heard, those folks turned that building into a hovel," she said. "I'm told it was filthy, with roaches everywhere. I hope you looked over that linoleum carefully before you bought it."

Grady nodded. "I did. Besides, it was never in the house. He had it stored in one of the sheds. It was a good bargain, Daisy."

Daisy sighed. "You're right. It's pretty and cheerful-looking. That poor woman, dying out there. Maybe the linoleum was the only pretty thing she had — and she never got to enjoy it. We are lucky, Grady!"

But Daisy was wrong. The luck of Mr. and Mrs. Grady Norman ended that day.

A few months later, Daisy became ill. She coughed and wheezed, her eyes and nose streamed. "Allergy," she decided, and threw away her feather pillows and quilts. But the symptoms persisted, and now Grady was suffering from them, too.

"Have you introduced anything new into your diets? Got yourself a new rug or upholstery?" asked the doctor they consulted. "It looks like an allergy, all right."

The Normans stared at each other. The linoleum! It occurred to them that their symptoms were always worse in the rooms where the linoleum had been put down.

The next day Grady and his son pulled up the linoleum.

"Look at that!" his son gasped.

That was a thick blanket of gray, scummy-looking mold covering the underside of the linoleum.

"Let's get it out of the house, quick!" Grady replied, swallowing his disgust.

They dragged it out into the yard and turned it over so that the sun could get at the mold. Then they scraped the musty-smelling stuff off with sticks.

"Let's burn the whole thing, Dad — it might spread." But Grady didn't agree. Now that the floor covering was scraped clean, he felt it still might be useful. Perhaps he could use it to patch shed roofs. He rolled it up and stored it in one of the outbuildings.

Inside the Norman house, Daisy had been frantically busy. She scrubbed down the floors and walls with hot water and detergent. Then she shellacked the area that the linoleum had covered. After all, shellac contained alcohol, and alcohol was a disinfectant.

26

"That should take care of that," she told herself. "Now we can relax."

But there was no relaxation in sight. It was the beginning of a long, long nightmare.

A few days later, Daisy awoke to streaky shadows on the walls of her bedroom. But the shadows didn't go away when the sun moved over the walls. They weren't shadows at all, but long, gray fingers of mold.

More desperate scrubbing and disinfecting. But it seemed that as soon as she cleaned the mold off one surface, it fastened on another. It spread over clothing, books, and furniture. When drawers were opened, they contained a layer of mold over their contents. In a matter of days, it was back on the floors, casting a grayish bloom over rugs and drapes. It even crept into the water pipes, infecting the water so that it made the skin burn and itch.

Like an army of three fighting an invasion, the Normans had no time to rest. They battled with boiling water, cleansers, germicides, disinfectants. Doors and windows were kept open in the hope that fresh air might kill the fungus. Their furniture was dragged outside to bake in the sunshine.

To remain in the house for any length of time became an agony. The mold made them cough and sneeze endlessly. Neighbors who came to help were driven away by spasms of coughing. When the minister came by to pray with them, the mold covered his Bible.

It seemed now that the mold had developed a musty, warning odor. First there was the smell, then the mold would appear. Daisy almost welcomed this new symptom. It gave her time to get her pails and brushes ready for the next outbreak. But there seemed to be no way the Normans could turn back the tide of battle. This was made very clear when their married daughter, Alma Jean, drove up to see them.

Alma Jean and her husband lived in Sparta, a good distance away. The drive had been a long, hot one, and Alma Jean wasn't feeling well by the time they got to the Normans. She decided to lie down and take a short nap on the living-room sofa.

Daisy and Grady felt uneasy. Their endless scrubbing, airing, and disinfecting seemed to have slowed down the mold in the last couple of days. But they knew their relief was only temporary. Still, there were chores to do. So the Normans and their son-in-law left Alma Jean and went off to do them. It was an hour before they finished and walked back to the house.

"There's that smell — " Grady began, his nose twitching. Then he and Daisy began to run.

The Normans rushed into the living room. Alma Jean was sitting up on the sofa, brushing mold from her dress. A thick furry coat of mold covered the sofa.

Grady half-lifted her off the sofa and took her quickly into the yard. By now, the smell was so thick that everyone was choking. The men tied handkerchiefs around the lower portions of their faces, and went back inside to carry out the sofa. There was no trace of mold anywhere else in the living room.

It was clear that the Norman war was over. The mold had won. The Normans moved out, setting up housekeeping in an old bus near the woods. In the deserted front yard, the furniture still stood, shrouded in mold that the sunshine no longer seemed able to kill.

For the Normans, their new peace was bitter. The County Health officials put up signs, warning everyone to stay off their property. "If I could sell the land, I'd buy a new place up near my son's," said Grady. "But buyers aren't exactly rushing in when they find out why those signs are there."

Most of the Normans' neighbors shunnned them. "It's as if they thought we had the plague," Daisy mourned. "Why, the dry cleaners won't even touch our clothes."

Some of the folks in the region think there must have been a curse on the linoleum, perhaps put there by a dying woman in a miserable hovel. "But why?" asked one of Grady's friends. "Why would a curse come to a good man like Grady Norman, who never did harm to anyone, anywhere? He lives by the Bible, as close as anybody you'll ever find. But it does seem strange. All that sickness and heartache and loss — without a reason!"

Was there a reason? A few people in Surrey County think there are witches in the region. Some say that perhaps the man who sold the linoleum to Grady was a witch. But the friends of the Normans laugh at that. "Witches are just notions," they will tell you. "We don't hold with that nonsense."

The mystery still remains. Where did the mold come from? Why were the Normans affected? Why did the mold never spread beyond the Norman household? And what will the people of Surrey County do if it does start to spread?

One man has an answer. "We'd have to burn everything it touched to ashes. Then we'd have to turn over every bit of earth it passed over, and sow the ground with salt. That's what you have to do when there's evil around. That's the only way to get rid of a curse."

WAMAGEMESWAK

In the days before the white man came to the Northeastern shores of America, the confederacy met regularly. Each year they came to the council fires — the men of the tribes of the Pequots, Penobscots, Delawares, Munsees, Narragansetts, and Mohicans.

At the council fires, they considered the future welfare of the tribes. But some who had visions said a bad time was coming. A strange race, numerous as leaves upon the trees, would come from the sunrise and crowd out the people of the confederacy.

Many refused to listen to these dreary prophecies. But one word was whispered, as if it was the name of a secret weapon which might be used if the invaders came.

The word was *wamagemeswak*.

31

* * * *

In the year 1751, John Stevens claimed a narrow stretch of land far up the Penobscot River. He felt a certain sympathy for the Indians who had been forced to leave it. It was good land, heavily timbered, with plenty of fresh water at hand. With his son, Martin, Stevens set to work to clear space on which he planned to build a house and plant crops.

As he worked, John saw in his mind a cabin raised, fields planted, smoke coming from a chimney. When Martin married, there would be room for his cabin, too. If all went well, he could send back to Boston by next spring for his wife, Molly. She hadn't been well lately, and John had left her there with her family.

One sultry afternoon as the two men worked, John noticed something new and strange. Everything around them seemed unnaturally quiet. The birds were hushed, there was no rustle of leaves. Even the sound of the river seemed muffled and far away.

He signaled Martin. Puzzled, the young man put down his axe.

"Listen, Martin. . . ."

"I hear nothing."

"That's just the point, lad. There's nothing to hear but the noise our axes are making. The place is as quiet as a tomb."

Martin cocked his head and listened. His own voice dropped to a whisper as he said, "You're right, Father. Why is it so, do you suppose?"

John shook his head. "These woods aren't like the woods back in England. They say the devil prowls them. It's the devil's own quiet, for sure." Then seeing that Martin was uneasy, John broke off with a short laugh. "Come on. We're scaring ourselves like a pair of old grannies. Maybe a storm is coming, and that's put a hush over things. Let's double our own noise and make the woods ring."

Welcoming a chance to work off their nervousness, the two men set to work cutting timber. By sundown, they were almost too tired to think. They built a fire and roasted a rabbit Martin had shot earlier in the day. When the meal was finished, it was all they could do to keep their eyes open long enough to bank the fire and make beds of dry leaves.

The moon was dropping behind the trees when John woke suddenly. A sharp pain in his right hand had yanked him back to consciousness. He opened his eyes just in time to see something thin and brown straighten up from his side and scuttle away into the underbrush.

Blood was trickling from his hand. He reached for his musket and jumped to his feet. Martin awoke as he fired.

"What is it, Father?"

"I don't know. Some animal, I think. Bit me on the hand, then ran off. I didn't get a good look at it."

"Your hand's bleeding. I'll get some water."

When Martin had washed away the blood, he whistled in dismay. "The beast took a wedge out of your hand. Just missed cutting the tendon. It's an odd shape for a bite."

And it was. The flesh looked as if it had been gouged, leaving a red cavity shaped like a triangle. Looking at it, John felt suddenly cold. What kind of an animal left a mark like that?

By morning, John's hand was red and swollen, and his eyes were glazed with fever. He mumbled about cutting more timber, but fell back when he tried to rise.

"It's no good, Father," Martin told him. "Whatever bit you left a poison. I'll put a poultice on it. But you must bide here and rest."

By afternoon, the red swelling was moving up John's arm, and he was tossing in delirium. "The wound should be cauterized," Martin told himself — and knew he would have to do it. He heated the edge of his axe in the hot coals. Then, setting his teeth, he applied it to the wound. John, out of his head with fever, scarcely seemed to notice.

When it grew dark, Martin built up the fire, and sat down with his father's musket to keep watch. From time to time, he bathed the sick man's face and forced water between his lips. Later, he wondered what would have happened if he had dropped off to sleep. But he didn't. And because worry and nerves kept him awake and alert, he saw the *wamagemeswak*.

At first it was just a glimpse out of the corner of his eye. Something very thin and brown, almost the height of a man, flashed into view — then vanished. Martin jumped to his feet. He looked directly at the spot under the trees where the thing had appeared. But now there was nothing there. Earlier he had made a rough torch of rags wound around the end of a stripped branch. He lit this now and held it aloft. Still nothing . . . just trees and undergrowth. . . .

No, wait! A flicker of movement. Then a thin brown shape, like a wizened old man. An Indian? No, more like some long-dead mummy. The figure stood sideways, not seeming to be aware of Martin. He got a quick impression of a hollow eye socket, a sunken profile, as if the creature had no nose.

His heart was thudding in his chest. "What do you want?" he croaked. "Who are you?"

It was like a conjuring trick. The thing started to turn in his direction — and disappeared!

With a single bound, Martin covered the distance between the fire and the spot where the thing had been. He moved the torch slowly back and forth so that even the darkness beyond the trees was lighted up. Nothing . . . no one. . . .

Then the hairs on the back of his neck began to prickle. He swung around. The thing was there, by the fire, bending over his father. He could see the hungry, caved-in profile. The dark hole that was its mouth was lined with tiny, pointed teeth.

Martin rushed forward, the torch held out like a lance. He saw the bony shape straighten, start to turn in his direction — and vanish. A current of cold air moved past him, and he felt a stinging pain in his left shoulder. He didn't need to look at it to know there would be a wedge-shaped bite there. He sat down by the fire, and reached for his axe.

The pain of the cauterization left him dizzy and sick. "I mustn't faint . . ." he told himself. "Must stay awake . . . keep watch. . . ." But it was no use. He toppled over into unconciousness.

Much later he opened his eyes. Even before he struggled to sit up, he knew that someone was watching him. An Indian girl was sitting beside his father, looking at him steadily.

To the end of his life, Martin was never sure that he actually heard her speak to him. Sometimes he thought her voice had only been in his mind. But he never forgot what she said.

"A canoe is waiting beyond. Take your father and go, or you will both die."

She stood up, then bent over him. Her eyes glittered in the firelight. "It will never be your land. *Wamagemeswak* guards it. *Wamagemeswak* will devour all whites who come here."

"Maybe it's a dream," Martin told himself. He remembered asking, "What is *wamagemeswak*?"

"A demon called up by those who know how to do such things. *Wamagemeswak* are always hungry. Hunger is all they know. No man can look them in the face, for they are so thin you can see them only from the side. Your fire-sticks cannot harm them, for they are already dead. No matter how many whites come to this place, *wamagemeswak* will destroy them all."

"Then why have you come to help us?"

"Many of my people say it is bad medicine to call up such as *wamagemeswak*. When it has finished with the whites, will it not turn on us? But this *wamagemeswak* is bound to this land by the river. It will not follow you.

"Now you must take your father and go. Never come back. Never let your children's children come back. Never sell the land. Hold it, keep it empty. No white man can come here and live."

The canoe was waiting where she said it would be. The river's current took the two men downstream to the settlement near Penobscot Bay. But Martin did not report his experience to anyone but his mother. Who else would believe such a tale?

Years later he set it all down on paper for his descendants to read. But in case they should think his mind was unsound, he made sure to first call in his lawyer. Papers were drawn up to make sure that the tract on the river would never be sold or occupied.

Today the tract is a fenced-in stretch of woodland. Trespassers are no problem because it is so thickly overgrown. But once the bones of a deer were found near the fence, with odd, wedge-shaped marks on them. Did the deer encounter a ravenous creature so thin that it could only be seen from the side?

DEMON ON NORTH DELAWARE STREET

For most Americans, March 11, 1962, was just another early spring day. But for Renata Beck and her 13-year-old daughter, Linda, it was the beginning of a very special reign of terror.

The Becks' home was a big, two-story house on North Delaware Street in Indianapolis. Renata and Linda shared the place with Renata's widowed mother, Mrs. Lina Gemmecke. Neighbors say it was not a happy household. Sounds of quarreling and shouting could often be heard coming from the house.

March 11, 1962, began peacefully. Renata and her mother had brought some pieces of crystal from Germany, and they cleaned and arranged them in different rooms in the house.

When Linda came home from school, the three settled down to a quiet dinner, followed by some TV watching.

At exactly 10:37 p.m., a terrific crash came from upstairs.

"The first thing I thought of was burglars," Renata remembers. "I thought someone must have slipped upstairs while the three of us were in the living room. There'd been a lot of robbery in this city. But when we ran upstairs, there was no one there. One of the pieces of crystal was lying on the floor about four feet from the bookcase where I had placed it — smashed to pieces, as if it had been thrown hard. I can't understand how it just fell off the bookcase and landed four feet away."

Renata cleaned up the breakage, and the three went back downstairs. Almost at once there was the sound of more crystal breaking in the next room. Then a heavy glass ashtray sailed past them and crashed against the wall.

Thoroughly frightened, the three ran to the kitchen. Renata called the police. Then she called two close friends of the family, Emil Noseda and his wife. Mr. Noseda advised her to spend the night in a hotel with her mother and daughter.

The next morning, the three women returned to the house on North Delaware Street. Everything was quiet when they entered. But 10 minutes later, the sound of breaking glass echoed upstairs and downstairs. Frantically, Renata called the police again. This time they sent Sergeant John Mullin.

"It was unbelievable," Mullin recalls. "The place was littered with broken glass. Mrs. Beck and her mother were terrified. So was the girl. I thought at first that the glass might have been broken by reverberations from a hi-fi record player. I've known that to happen. But there wasn't a hi-fi in the house — only a small, kid's record player stowed away in a closet. Then I checked out the premises to see if someone might have fired a pellet gun through the windows. But the storm windows were up, and not one had a crack in it."

Determined to solve the mystery, the police brought in high frequency sound gear. But their tests could detect nothing that might have caused the breakage. Meanwhile, more police were brought on the scene to control the crowds which had begun gathering outside the house ever since the stories of the disturbances on North Delaware Street had made the newspapers.

Patrolman Ray Patton was stationed inside the Beck house. He was with the three women when a crash came from Linda's bedroom. When he investigated, he found a large, green, glass ornament lying smashed in the middle of the floor.

A couple of days later, Renata Beck began to wonder again about burglars. Her leather case, containing $125, vanished. Reporters joined the police in a search, going over every inch of the house and grounds. But there was no sign of the case or the money.

One afternoon, Renata asked Patton to

come upstairs with her. "I want to show you something," she said. She went to a dresser in her room and lifted up a large hat lying on top. Underneath there were three beautiful crystal goblets. "I had six of these an hour ago," she whispered. "Something smashed three of them. That's why I hid the rest under my hat."

But the goblets were doomed. As Patton left the room, one of them sailed off the dresser and hit him in the back. Then it fell to the floor and broke into pieces. A few minutes later, a second goblet caromed off and smashed against the wall.

Within a few days, there wasn't a bit of crockery or glassware unbroken in the house. The unseen force began to play with the cutlery.

"All of us, including my wife, were sitting in the living room," recalls Mr. Noseda. "We heard a lot of racket in the kitchen. We rushed out and found three knives lying on the floor in the form of a cross. They had been in a drawer about three feet from where we found them. We put them all back into the drawer, and went back into the living room. A few minutes later, we heard the sounds in the kitchen again. The knives were back on the floor in the form of a cross. I've never seen anything like it!"

Nor had anyone present ever seen anything like what happened next. Noseda recalls the scene vividly. "We were sitting on the couch, and all of us were talking about the damage that had been done. Suddenly Mrs. Gemmecke grabbed her throat and gasped, 'They're choking me!' A policeman and I grabbed her hands and pulled them down. On her throat were two sets of tiny punctures. They looked like little teeth marks, but they didn't bleed."

In the days that followed, the punctures appeared on Mrs. Gemmecke eight more times. "Mrs. Beck was bitten twice," says Noseda," and puncture marks also appeared on Linda's hands and arms." One policeman said the marks looked like bat bites.

"The flesh around the punctures turned black and blue," says Noseda. "But the women said there was no pain, and they had no after-effects. I saw those bites, and so did many other people who were present."

In the midst of all these frightening events, the leather case reappeared. According to Mrs. Gemmecke, she felt something nudge her leg, and when she looked down — there it was! But on its return, the case contained only $35 of the missing $125.

On March 26, neighbors called the police. They complained that someone at the Beck house was disturbing the peace. Shouts, screams, and sounds of objects being thrown were heard.

When the police arrived, they found Mrs. Gemmecke lying unconscious on the floor. "She's in a diabetic coma," explained Renata.

What happened next was unexpected. A

heavy tray was thrown at the officers, and a piano bench mysteriously overturned. One police officer claimed he saw Mrs. Gemmecke do it. She was arrested and taken to jail. The next day she was released on bond — on condition that she go back to her native Germany. She packed up and left.

Some people say that Mrs. Gemmecke was the real force behind the disturbances on North Delaware Street. But they can't explain how she could have moved objects in one room while she sat in another.

Mr. Noseda believes none of the women had anything to do with what happened in the Beck house. "I know from what I saw and heard that no one in the house could have done all the things that took place. There was something else — some force that hated those women and deliberately broke up their belongings. It happened over and over again while all of us, including Mrs. Gemmecke, were together in one room.

"I don't know what the force was, or how it operated. But I saw it in action. I never want to go through such experiences again."

Since Mrs. Gemmecke went back to Germany, things have been quiet at the Beck house. But the mystery is still unsolved. Who or what wrecked the household? Who or what left punctures on the arms and necks of three frightened women?

THE TYPEWRITER THAT FORETOLD DOOM

The rain fell steadily, making a beaded curtain across the windshield. Harry Lang slowed the car to a crawl along the rutted road. Although he was returning home from a party, he felt depressed and fearful. "Shouldn't have had that last drink," he told himself.

The light was fading. It would be dark before he got home. "Won't be able to see where I'm going," he muttered, then laughed dismally. The truth was that he hadn't been able to see where he was going for the last five years. Here he was, almost 30, with no past worth speaking of, and no future in sight. He had held a few jobs, but none of them led anywhere. He had written a few poems, but none of them had been published. The "home" he was heading for didn't even belong to him. It was a beach house loaned to him by a friend for a month.

Until now, Harry hadn't worried about the future. He had drifted along, just getting by. But on this June night in 1940, he started to worry. Maybe that was why he made a wrong turn and crashed head on into a truck.

"You've got no business being alive," the doctor told him at the hospital. It was true. Here he was with broken ribs, a broken leg, and a bad concussion. But he was alive. The car he had been driving, on the other hand, was a total wreck.

Somehow Harry felt less depressed than he had just before the accident. His bones would mend, and maybe his life would, too. He'd already had a little bit of luck — a letter from an old friend, Arthur Stellings.

Stellings was the editor of a small magazine. When he heard about Harry's accident, he wrote out of sympathy. He suggested that since Harry was laid up in bed, he might pass the time by writing a short story. Maybe, Stellings hinted, it would be good enough to publish in the magazine.

Of course Stellings never expected Harry to follow through. In his opinion, Harry had no talent and no ambition. But two months later he got a story called "Disaster" from Harry. "Sorry this took so long. I had to wait until I could get hold of a typewriter. This one is a real antique, but it works. The guy who sold it to me said it used to belong to a *Boston Globe* reporter named Ed Samson. Did you ever hear of him?"

Ed Samson. The odd thing was that Stellings had heard of the reporter. In 1883, he had written down a dream of a terrible volcanic eruption in Krakotoa. Every detail of his dream had come true — days later.

Stellings smiled and shook his head. Harry was probably just making up that stuff about Samson's typewriter. Did he really have a gift for fiction? He picked up Harry's story and began to read it.

It was astonishingly good. He could scarcely believe Harry had written it. It told of a terrible earthquake in Angola, and how the disaster affected the members of a small tribe. Harry had written it with such sympathy and understanding that It was hard to believe he hadn't lived through the disaster himself.

Stellings knew literary talent when he saw it. He wrote Harry, asking for more stories. He also suggested that Harry move in with him.

At first it was a good arrangement. Harry moved his few possessions and his battered typewriter into Stellings' Los Angeles apartment. He turned out another story. Like the first, it was excellent. And like the first story, it also told of a disaster. This time the location was Mexico, and the victims poor peasants. But once again the writing was so powerful and so real that the story seemed like an eyewitness account.

When the stories were published, Harry became famous overnight. He was invited to parties — lots of parties. He went to so many of them that Stellings began to worry. Harry wasn't spending enough time working, in Stellings' opinion. He was also beginning to drink too much again. Stellings decided it was time for some fatherly advice.

"Harry, you've got to cut down on your social life. You're a fine writer, but you haven't touched the typewriter for months. Your talent is going to dry up if you don't get back to work."

Harry stared at him blearily. "Don't worry, pal. I'm just having a little fun. You want me to write something? O.K. All I have to do is sit down at my trusty old typewriter, and out it comes. I can do it drunk or sober."

Disgusted, Stellings went to bed. But the sound of Harry typing drunkenly away went on for hours.

In the morning, Stellings found typed pages in an envelope on the breakfast table. "Drunken drivel," he muttered, but took the pages with him when he went to the office.

Later on in the day, Stellings remembered the envelope. He took it out and began to read the pages. His anger at Harry turned to admiration. The story, called "Fear," was a work of genius. It told about a man who was terribly afraid of something he couldn't see or describe. This fear weighed him down and finally made him kill himself. It was so vividly written that Stellings broke out into a cold sweat as he read it.

When "Fear" was published, Harry was called one of the most promising writers of the 20th century. But there was nothing more to promise. "Fear" turned out to be the last story he would ever write.

A few days later, Stellings was reading the morning newspaper. A headline caught his eye — "Disaster in Angola!" A volcanic eruption, followed by an earthquake, had wiped out a forest-dwelling tribe, and devastated the countryside. Almost line for line the place, names, and events were the way Harry had described them months ago in his first story.

When he saw the newspaper, Harry turned pale. "But I wrote fiction," he muttered. "I invented the disaster and the people. How could I know it would happen?"

Stellings tried to soothe him. "It's just a crazy coincidence. You're not a prophet — just a very creative writer. Come on, forget about it. Let's start thinking about your next story."

But there would be no next story. Harry was avoiding the typewriter. After March, he avoided the newspapers, too. Under a March dateline there was shocking news from Mexico. The Rio de Nazas had flooded, drowning scores of people. The story Harry had written months before might have been a reporter's account of the event. Even the names of the victims matched those in his story.

"I'm never writing another line, Arthur," he told Stellings. "If I do, it will come true. I'll be responsible for the deaths of innocent people."

"Look, Harry, what you need is a vacation. Why don't you drive to the desert — someplace different, where you can think things out? Find a nice quiet place to stay," Stellings suggested.

To his surprise, Harry agreed. He even stowed the old typewriter in the car.

But Stellings noticed that Harry didn't look like a man anticipating a happy vacation. His face was set and drawn. And his eyes seemed haunted.

As Stellings had suggested, Harry drove south. Beyond the Los Angeles city limits, he began to drive faster and faster, as if trying to outrun something. He crossed the Mexican border, speeding into the foot hills beyond.

A few days later, news came to Stellings that Harry was dead. In broad daylight, he had driven his car over a cliff. Like the hero of his last story, he had found the only way to escape his gift of prophecy was to die. And he had taken Ed Samson's typewriter with him.

THE WONDER HORSES OF ELBERFELD

According to animal psychologists, horses are not overly-intelligent. Dolphins, whales, monkeys, dogs, and perhaps even cats rate higher marks when it comes to brains. But there are exceptions to every rule. In 1910, the exceptions were the horses of Elberfeld.

It all began in a small town in Germany. The people there awoke one morning to find posters on the town walls announcing a circus. It was only a small circus. The posters promised a juggler, a fire-eater, a dancing bear. They also made it plain that there would be an extra added attraction — *Fritz Krell and His Equine Wizards*!

"Must be some kind of magic act," said one old man. " 'Equine' means horses, doesn't it? What kind of magic can you do with horses?"

Since there were few amusements in the town, the circus was a sellout. But by the time the dancing bear had finished, the crowd was getting restless. Horses were nothing new to them, they said to each other. There was a lot of shuffling of feet and clearing of throats.

Then a thin-faced man in an elegant riding habit stepped out before them, followed by three horses. But these were not circus animals. They were proud, magnificent creatures — a chestnut gelding and two Arab stallions.

"Ladies and gentlemen," the man said, "permit me to introduce myself. I am Fritz Krell, and these are my collegues. This is Berto — " and the chestnut gelding stepped forward. "These gentlemen" — he pointed to the Arab stallions — "are Zarif and Muhammed. Berto will begin our show. What is the sum of five and four?"

Berto rapped out the answer to that and other problems in addition by stamping the correct number of times with his left front hoof. Next Zarif stepped forward to show that he could not only add, but multiply, subtract, and divide. He showed he meant hundreds by nodding his head; tens by stamping his left front hoof; and single units by stamping his right front hoof.

Krell saved the best for the last. Muhammed stepped into the center of the ring. "Give the square root of 81!" Krell ordered. Muhammed stamped nine times with his right front hoof.

Before the crowd could catch its breath,

Krell put Muhammed through a dazzling number of problems in square and cube roots. In every case, the Arab stallion gave the correct answers. The crowd burst into applause.

But Krell held up a hand for silence. He brought out a set of alphabet blocks and spread them before Muhammed.

"What is your name?" asked Krell.

"M-U-H-A-M-M-E-D," the horse spelled by picking up the correct blocks in its teeth, then laying them in front of Krell.

"Where do you come from?"

"E-L-B-E-R-F-E-L-D."

"Who was your father?"

"Kluge (Clever) Hans."

The crowd gasped. They had heard of the wonderful Arab stallion, Clever Hans. He had been trained by William von Ostend, owner of a well-known riding school in Elberfeld. The abilities of Clever Hans were so astounding that a panel of experts, thinking his act was a fraud, examined the horse carefully for months. At the end of that time, one of the experts, a Professor E. Clarapede of the University of Geneva, wrote:

"Hans could do more than mere sums. He knew how to read. He could also distinguish between harmonious and dissonant chords of music. He had an amazing memory; he could tell the date of each day of the current week. In short, he could do all the tasks that an intelligent schoolboy of 14 is able to perform."

What the crowd at the circus didn't know

was that Berto and Zarif were also sired by Hans. Nor did they know that the three wonder horses had a sister, Hanschen, who was equally intelligent.

Fritz Krell himself had worked as an assistant to von Ostend. From von Ostend he learned to train horses with love, not fear. No whip was ever allowed in the Elberfeld stables. William von Ostend treated his horses as though they were especially gifted children.

When von Ostend died in 1909, he left his riding school and his horses to Krell. In a short time, Krell sold the stables and found homes for most of the horses. But he kept the four foals of Clever Hans.

The small town circus was only the start for Krell and his wonder horses. Before long the act was shown all over Europe. The horses became famous and Krell became rich. But no one could say that he spent much of the money on himself. Most of it went for the care and maintainance of his horse stars.

During one tour, a famous Belgian writer, Maurice Maeterlink, asked to be allowed to call on Muhammed. When he entered the stable, Krell remained outside. While the astonished writer watched, Muhammed picked out alphabet blocks and spelled out Maeterlink's name.

"What is the square root of 59?" asked Maeterlink. Muhammed made no reply at first. Then, using the blocks, the horse spelled out,

"Fifty-nine has no square root. But it is a prime number."

Maeterlink was convinced, but some European scientists demanded that Krell let them test the horses in a special way. Krell was ordered to leave the area. Then telephone headphones were fitted over the horses' ears so that the scientists could ask questions from a distance. The horses came up with the correct answers.

Next, the horses were put into a stable with a blackboard. Questions were written on the blackboard, and the stable was locked. When it was unlocked, Clever Hans' clever children had spelled out the right answers with the blocks.

But Muhammed took a dislike to one scientist. He refused to answer any of the man's questions. The scientist sent for Krell.

"Why are you being so stubborn?" Krell asked the horse.

Muhammed's head dipped to his blocks. "This man hit Hanschen when she made a wrong answer. I will answer no more questions until he leaves," he spelled out.

In 1912 and 1913, two scientists named Schoeller and Gebrke reported that Muhammed seemed to be making efforts to imitate speech. After a few tries, he went back to his blocks and spelled, "I have not a good voice."

What became of the Elberfeld horses? They vanished, with Fritz Krell, during World War I. When the war was over, scientists went to

Germany in search of them. But where their stables had stood there were only the ruins of a war plant.

It is possible that the horses died during the war. But it is also possible that Krell took them away, perhaps to safety in Switzerland. Wherever they went, they took with them the secret of their almost-human intelligence.

A VISITOR TO DEVON

What kind of a creature can travel 100 miles in a single night, move in a straight line no matter what gets in its way, and leave tracks exactly eight inches apart?

No one has been able to answer this question for 124 years. It's likely that no one will ever be able to answer it. But there is evidence that such a creature did exist — and may still exist.

On the night of February 7, 1855, heavy snow fell over Devon, a county in southwest England. The flakes were the size of feathers, and they fell so thickly that it was impossible to see a handsbreadth ahead. As a result, people got indoors and stayed there. The strange visitor who came had the Devon countryside to itself.

The snowfall ended before midnight. As far as the eye could see, the county lay buried under an unbroken blanket of white. Or an almost unbroken blanket. Threading across fields, hills, downs, and the towns of Topsham, Lympstone, Exmouth, Dawlish, and Teignmouth were tracks. What's more, they were like no tracks the people of Devon had ever seen before.

In shape, the tracks resembled hoofprints, but of an unknown animal. They measured four inches in length, and were about two and three-quarters of an inch across. They ran in a straight line, each print directly eight inches behind the other. They also not only ran across ground level, but straight up walls and over rooftops. And as if that wasn't enough to puzzle over, the tracks crossed 100 miles of the county to the water's edge on the Bristol Channel — then for a few yards on the other side of the Channel!

The first man to see the tracks was a Topsham baker. He followed them across the snow to the door of his bake shop, where they suddenly made a right angle turn and went up and over a five-foot wall. As it turned out, there was scarcely any house in town that hadn't been visited by the mysterious creature. According to an article in the *London Times*, "The footprints were seen in all kinds of inaccessible places — on housetops, on walls of enclosed gardens and courtyards, as well as in open fields. There was hardly a garden in the area where the prints were not observed.

"The distance between the prints was always exactly eight inches. These regular tracks passed over roofs, hayricks, and walls as high as 14 feet without disturbing the snow on either side."

Photographs of the prints appeared in the *Illustrated London News* of February 24, 1855. The prints' precise line made them look as though they had been stamped out by some ghostly cookie cutter.

Several scientists offered explanations. One said the tracks had been made by an escaped kangaroo. Another suggested that a one-legged bird was responsible. No one tried to explain how a kangaroo could grow hooves, or a one-legged bird hop 100 miles.

The people of Devon had an explanation of their own. Only the Devil, they said, could make prints like those.

By March the snow and the prints were gone in Devon. But on the Polish border, near Galacia, the same kind of prints marked up the snow. A reporter from the *Illustrated London News* went to Poland to check out the tracks and get the reactions of witnesses. He wrote: "The inhabitants believe the tracks to be caused by supernatural influences."

Across the Atlantic, in New Jersey, an

American version of the Devon Devil took off. It not only left little hoofprints in the snow, but was said to yowl like a banshee.

Unlike the Devon Devil, the New Jersey version had a pedigree. According to some old timers in Estelville, New Jersey, it had been born in their town. It seemed that a Mrs. Leeds, expecting her seventh baby, said she would rather have a devil. When the child was born, it was said to have cloven hooves, a long tail, the face of a horse, the body of a kangaroo, and the wings of a bat. After arriving in the world, it snorted fire and smoke, and disappeared up the chimney.

Right up into the early 1900's, New Jerseyites were complaining about their local devil. But it took a man named Norman Jeffries to put the creature into show business.

Mr. Jeffries was a press agent. In 1906, he worked for Brandenbur's Arch Street Museum in Philadelphia. He read about Mrs. Leeds and her unusual offspring in an old book, and decided that the Jersey Devil was just what the Arch Street Museum needed to bring in the customers. Then he leaked a hot news item to the newspapers. The Jersey Devil had been captured, and would be on exhibit at the Museum.

Crowds rushed to buy tickets. When the curtain went up, they weren't disappointed. A luminous green thing with short front legs, powerful hindquarters, and bat wings leaped onstage. The customers ran for the exit. This made room for the next batch of ticketbuyers.

For weeks the Jersey Devil was a star. Then the truth leaked out. The ghastly green thing really was a kangaroo. Jeffries had painted it with luminous green paint, and strapped it into a harness with metal wings attached. None of the spectators ever stayed around long enough to look at it closely.

But it's hard to keep a good monster down. As late as 1960, New Jersey police got calls about unexplained tracks and unearthly yowlings — all blamed on the Jersey Devil.

In Devon, however, the weird unseen visitor has never returned — not unless you count what happened to the Reverend Joseph Overs on August 11, 1954.

Overs was strolling along the beach on Lundy Island in the Bristol Channel. Suddenly he stumbled over an object lying half out of a tidal pool. He took a closer look, and rushed off to call the police. When they came to look, they called in scientific experts.

What lay on the beach was about four feet long, and weighed a hefty 25 pounds. It was some kind of marine animal because it had gills. It also had a wide mouth full of sharp teeth, big round eyes, and pink skin. It had been dead for several days.

What really puzzled the experts were the thing's legs and feet. It had two short, sturdy legs placed so that it could walk upright. The five toes of each foot were arranged in a U-shape around a center arch.

Prints were made of the feet — prints that looked oddly like hoofprints.

The Reverend Overs' discovery adds up to a double mystery. What was the thing he found on the beach? And did it have any connection with Devon's mystery visitor of February 7, 1855?

MASTER OF THE DEAD

Not all tourists who went to Haiti in the 1950's met Andre Vincent, but a lot of them did. Andre was an old man who claimed to know more about the island than anyone alive. He hung around the hotels in Port-au-Prince and invited tourists to visit his house in the hills. Hotel managers always warned the tourists not to go. They said that Andre was not quite right in the head, and besides, his house was old and falling to pieces.

Bill King was warned about Andre the first day he arrived in Port-au-Prince. The captain of the cruise ship told him about the old man as Bill was preparing to go ashore. "He is sure to single you out because you are an American, and because you have come to make recordings of Haitian songs. I should advise you not to accept his invitation."

"Why?" asked Bill, who didn't like being told what to do.

"Well, there is nothing wrong with Andre. He's old, but he's interesting to talk to. People say he's crazy, but that's not true. What's wrong with Andre is Celestine, his daughter. Nobody will have anything to do with her — and neither should you."

"Why not?"

"Well, it's probably just superstitious nonsense. I've said too much already." And the captain refused to say any more.

A few hours later, Bill was having lunch at his hotel when a shadow fell across the table. A tall old man stood there.

"I am Andre Vincent," he said. "I can help you."

Bill felt confused. "I don't understand."

The old man smiled. "This is not a large island, and news travels fast. Everyone already knows that a young American has come to record the songs of my people. I can take you where you will need to go."

"I'm sorry," Bill replied. "I can't afford a guide."

"No, no," the old man protested. "I would be insulted if you offered me money. I know every inch of Haiti, and most of the people who live here. Therefore, I regard it as my business to make it known to others — especially visitors who come seeking knowledge."

Bill was beginning to like the old man. "Thank you," he said. "I'll be grateful for your help."

"Good. I will call for you tomorrow morning. I suggest you bring your equipment and your luggage. Travel in the hills is slow, and we may be gone several days." He bowed and left the room.

A few minutes later, the hotel manager came to Bill's table. "I am sorry, sir. I did not mean for Andre Vincent to annoy you," he said nervously.

"He didn't annoy me at all. He was very kind. He offered to take me into the hills to make recordings."

"Don't misunderstand me, sir," said the manager earnestly. "Mr. Vincent is a respected citizen. He has written many books about Haiti. But he is old, and not a good driver. It would be best if you did not let him take you out of Port-au-Prince."

Bill began to feel irritated. "What is all this about? This is the second time today I've been warned about Vincent. You said yourself that he's respectable."

"It's just that it would be wise not to go to his home," the manager stammered. "Like Andre, the place is old and decrepit. The floors are rotting — you could have an accident. No one goes there. You are a stranger, and you don't understand. . . ."

Suddenly the manager stopped talking and looked at the doorway. Andre Vincent was standing there, watching him. The manager muttered an apology to Bill and walked quickly out of the room. Bill noticed that he didn't even look at Vincent as he brushed by.

The old man bowed to Bill. "Perhaps you would like to come with me now, Mr. King. My car is outside. I have taken the liberty of having your baggage put in it. You must not mind that ignorant man. The staff of this hotel are meddlesome and superstitious. They think they are building up Haiti's glamour by making tourists nervous."

Bill says now that he should have had a sense of foreboding. But he didn't. "Andre Vincent seemed so sensible that I trusted him on sight. The manager, on the other hand, seemed to be on the edge of a nervous break-down. Vincent had this old Rolls Royce parked outside. It looked as battered and ancient as he did, but like him, it had real style."

So Bill got willingly into the car, and Vincent drove out of Port-au-Prince. It turned out that the manager had lied when he said the old man was a poor driver. Vincent drove carefully and well, making the bad roads fairly easy to take.

After about an hour, the car turned off the main road onto a rough track that wound upward through dusty brown hills. It was not an interesting ride. Every now and then a chicken or a small, ragged child would dart across the road. Bill couldn't help feeling that they just might be the only two live adult humans for miles. He also couldn't help feeling bored.

Because he was bored, he didn't feel startled when the big, ramshackle house came into view.

"Yours?" he asked.

Andre nodded. "You don't mind if we stop here? My daughter will have prepared lunch. We will eat and rest, then we will drive to Ansa-a-gallats. There is to be a festival there tonight, with much singing."

As the Rolls pulled up to the house, Bill could see that the hotel manager had been right about its condition. One of the pillars beside the front door had fallen down. The few shutters left at the windows hung at crazy angles. But once it had been an important-looking place, a place whose owners had to be rich.

Entering, Bill remembered the manager's warning about accidents. He walked very carefully. It would be all too easy to put a foot through the sagging floor and break a leg.

A door at the opposite end of the hall led into a garden. A young woman in a white dress stood there. Bill thought she might have been pretty if her features weren't so blunt, and her eyes so vague. She held her head on one side as if there was something wrong with her neck.

"My daughter, Celestine," said Andre. "My dear, this is Bill King, from the United States. He will have lunch with us."

Although Celestine was facing him, Bill got the impression that she didn't really see him. Nor did she respond to his greeting. Was it possible that she was blind and deaf? Her face was without expression. She gave no sign of having heard her father.

After a moment, she turned and went into the garden. The two men followed. A table was set for lunch there.

All through the meal, the girl never sat down. She moved back and forth between the garden and the house, bringing food and drink. Bill looked closely at her face as she set a plate before him. He noticed that her eyes seemed filmed over. She must be blind. But if she was, it didn't hinder her movements about the place.

Another thing that struck him as strange was her youth. She didn't look more than 20. Yet Andre himself must be well into his 80's.

"Forgive me," Bill said. "Your daughter seems so young. . . ."

Andre smiled. "She is not exactly what she seems. She is perhaps 20 years older than you think she is — perhaps more. But she lost the power to see many years ago, so the troubles of the world do not weigh on her. I think that has kept her young."

"Is she also deaf?"

"Almost. She can hear me if I speak in a certain tone. She cannot hear you."

"But she seems to know I am here."

"I have told her you are. She can sense your location."

"It must be lonely here for her."

"No. She does not know what it is to be lonely."

"Don't you ever take her into town?"

"She would not be welcome there," Andre muttered. "People are unkind and stupid. Now, please excuse me. I must pack some things for the trip."

He went into the house. Bill sat at the table, feeling drowsy. He doesn't remember falling asleep. But the shadows were long when he awoke with a start. Vincent was nowhere in sight, but Celestine was bending over him. Her hands were on his shoulders.

For a minute he stared at her. Her expression never changed, but the pressure of her hands increased. He was surprised to realize how strong she was. He began to be afraid that he couldn't break her hold.

The pressure kept increasing, forcing him out of the chair and onto his knees.

"Let me go!" he shouted. But now she was leaning all her weight on her hands. Dull shocks of pain were running down his arms.

"Vincent!" he screamed.

Then he heard Vincent's voice from the doorway. "Let him go!"

Celestine straightened up and moved away. Bill rubbed his aching shoulders. "What made her do that?" he gasped.

"She meant no harm. Perhaps you were

right — she is lonely. No one has come here in many years. You are our first guest. I think she wanted you to stay."

Bill felt he had had enough. "Would you mind taking me back to the hotel?"

"You do not wish to go to the festival tonight?"

"No. I want to go back to Port-au-Prince."

The old man's face crumpled as if he was about to cry. "Please, Mr. King, don't be angry. Let me explain about Celestine. Perhaps when you understand, you will be our friend.

"My daughter is not the young woman she appears to be. There are people who say she died 50 years ago."

Bill looked at him in horror. "What are you saying?"

"No, no, my friend," Vincent replied soothingly. "Of course that isn't true. But she was very ill, very close to death at that time. The doctors had given her up, and so had I. But Odette, an old woman who had been her nurse, wouldn't give up.

"I will never forget that day. Toward afternoon Celestine began to sink. There was no pulse, no sign of life that I could see. We thought she was dead, and we drew the sheet over her. Then Odette burst into the room. With her was a man I never wanted in my house. The hill folk called him Maitre Carrefour.

"They pushed me out of the room and locked the door. After what seemed a long time,

Odette opened it. 'She will live,' she said. The man came out. He was putting a small bottle into his pocket. He laughed and said, 'Your daughter will be with you for many years.' Then he went away, and I have never seen him since.

"It was true. Celestine lived, but it has not been a real life for her. She has been as she is now since that day — unable to see or hear, scarcely aware of the world around her. She never speaks. In some ways I think it is worse for us both than if she had died. For a long time she would obey only Odette. But when Odette died, she seemed to turn to me. She has never harmed anyone, but people are afraid of her. What will become of her when I die? Who will care for her?

"Mr. King, this is why I brought you here today. When you go back to America, please take my poor child with you. There are doctors there who might help her. I have money. I can pay for it." He leaned closer, to peer into Bill's face. "No, I can see it is no use. You are afraid of her, too."

"I couldn't control her. You must bring her yourself, put her into a hospital," Bill said urgently.

The old man shook his head. "It's no use. I was foolish to ask you such a favor. I think I knew all along that they would never let us leave Haiti."

"Who wouldn't?"

"Those in Port-au-Prince who were once

our friends. You see, too many of them believe that when Maitre Carrefour restored my poor child to life, he drew her soul into a bottle as payment and took it with him. They say he turned her into a zombie, and they are afraid to offend him by helping her."

"But zombies are just superstition, and anyway, the man is probably dead by now."

"If he is," the old man replied sadly, "there will be another Maitre Carrefour to fear. 'Maitre Carrefour' is a title for he who can master the dead. Sometimes such a one is called Legba-Petro. The Petro gods are terrible. If they do you a service, you must pay for it with a death. Usually a dead animal will do, but there have been cases . . . There! You see, I am talking like those fools in Port-au-Prince. I know there is an explanation — a reasonable explanation — for Celestine's condition, if I could only find it."

Vincent drove Bill back to his hotel, but the trip was a silent one. The two never talked again. One day before he left Haiti, Bill saw the old Rolls Royce drive past him. Vincent sat at the wheel, staring straight ahead. Beside him sat Celestine, her blank face shadowed by a wide-brimmed hat. As they passed, people drew back, pointing and whispering.

"It was as though Vincent was defying them all by bringing her into town — as if he was saying, 'What does it matter anymore?' " Bill recalls. "It was one of the saddest things I ever saw. But I still can't help thinking about

what Vincent told me. Then I wonder something really crazy. Do you suppose Maitre
Carrefour still has that bottle he took out of
Celestine's room that day? Do you suppose
there could really be *something* in the bottle?"

THE STRANGE CASE OF JOHANNES CUNTIUS

Silesia, a region in central Europe, had an unusual claim to fame in the 16th century. It was noted for its vampires.

Travelers to Silesia brought back strange tales. They reported that many villages had garlic hanging over the doors of houses and around the necks of cattle to keep vampires away. A German visitor wrote: "The vampires are said to come out of their graves in the nighttime, rush upon people sleeping in their beds, and destroy them. Those who are destroyed by them, after their deaths, become vampires. To prevent spreading this evil, stakes are driven through the bodies of the newly-dead."

In the town of Breslav, a shoemaker who

had committed suicide became a legal problem. A number of townspeople complained that the shoemaker was now a vampire, and wouldn't let them get any sleep. He would appear beside their beds, and bite and pinch and hit them. Soon half the town was staying up all night, huddled together in their dining rooms with the lights of candles blazing away.

The victims demanded that the shoemaker's body be dug up and destroyed. The widow said no. Finally the victims sued for the right to open the grave, and won.

The grave was opened in the presence of the town magistrate. To almost no one's surprise, the body wasn't even slightly decomposed although it had been in the ground since September, and it was now the following April.

For six days, the shoemaker was placed on view under guard. But in spite of the guard, people complained that the vampire still tormented them.

"Let's bury him under the town gallows," suggested the magistrate. "I've heard that's a good way to put a stop to a vampire."

He was wrong. A few days later the shoemaker's widow appealed to the town council. "You were right," she sobbed. "My husband is a vampire, and now he doesn't even spare his own family. I will no longer be against you if you want to take drastic measures."

Out came the shovels, and the shoemaker was again dug up. Onlookers couldn't help remarking that he looked healthier than he ever had in life.

How do you kill a vampire? The people of Breslav didn't do anything by halves. They cut off the head and arms. They destroyed its heart, then burnt the remains to ashes. Then the ashes were swept carefully together and thrown in the river. Then everybody went home and got the first good night's sleep they had had in months. As for the shoemaker, he seemed to be at last laid to rest.

It wasn't that easy to put an end to Johannes Cuntius.

Johannes was an alderman in the town of Pentsch. He was also a prosperous business-man and a solid citizen. It was not at all un-usual for the mayor to invite him over for supper.

But there were stories and rumors about this 60-year-old solid citizen. He never went to church, and people held this against him. It was said that he didn't dare enter the church because he had once made a contract with the devil. He had started out in life by hauling goods in his wagon for anyone who would pay a fee. But in a surprisingly short time, he had bought a number of wagons and gotten rich. He now had a stable full of fine horses, and a comfortable house. How, people asked, had he gotten so rich so fast without devilish help?

Envy can make people suspicious. One of Johannes's sons had disappeared years ago.

If Johannes had been a poor man, his neighbors might have felt sorry for him. Instead, rumors spread that he had given the boy to the devil as part of his terrible bargain.

Two days before he died, Johannes met the mayor in the street.

"Come to dinner, my friend," said the mayor. "I've got some problems with certain merchants, and I can use your advice."

"I'll be there," Johannes promised, "but first I must go home and tend to some business of my own. But it is good to be merry while we can. Troubles are growing up around us fast enough."

Later on the mayor remembered those last two sentences. He wondered if Johannes had a premonition that he was going to die.

As soon as he got home, Johannes went out to the stable. One of his prize horses had slipped a shoe, and he wanted to look at its foot. He commanded a servant to tie the horse to a post, and bent over the beast's hoof. Suddenly, the horse seemed to go crazy. It screamed, reared, and lashed out with its front feet, kicking Johannes in the head.

He lived for two days, thrashing about in his bed, and crying out that he was guilty of unpardonable sins. But when his sons offered to get the pastor, the dying man grew hysterical. "No priest can help me now!" he shouted.

On the night of the second day, his oldest son sat by Johannes's bed. At three in the morning, the old man seemed to slip into a coma, and the room was quiet. Then the scratching at the window began.

The son jumped up to look out. As he did so, the window flew open violently and a large black cat leaped into the room. It jumped up on the bed and scratched the dying man's face. Then it clawed at his body as if to drag it out of the bed.

Horrified, the young man grabbed at the animal. He thought he had his hands on it — but it was gone! A chill of fear crawled over him. This was a very bad omen, he knew. At that moment, he realized that his father was dead.

But neither he nor his brothers told anyone else about the cat's visit. They said that Johannes had scratched himself in his delirium, and they talked the pastor of the parish into letting the old man be buried near the church.

The funeral was almost as hair-raising as the death-bed. A howling windstorm arose as Johannes was carried to his grave. But as soon as he was interred, the storm died and the sun came out.

Trouble began the next night. The town watchman reported all kinds of strange goings-on at the dead man's house. The locked gates in front of the place suddenly burst open — though no one could be seen. There were sounds of things falling in the house and furniture being thrown about. Then Johannes's booming voice was heard shouting, "I can scarcely keep myself from beating you to death!'' Shortly afterward, the dogs all over town began to howl and bark.

The next night the disturbances shifted to the mayor's house. The sound of animals trampling around outside the place brought the servants out of their beds. Then great blows were struck on the outside walls, so that the whole house shook. In the morning, the ground outside was covered with ''the impressions of strange feet, that were like no creatures we knew.''

For eight long months, the spirit of Johannes drove his hometown to distraction. He would appear at the bedsides of relatives and friends. Sometimes he bit them on the neck and tried to drink their blood. At other times it was said that he dragged them out of bed and flung them around the room. He was accused of beating one child to death.

When Johannes the Vampire was in a good mood, he galloped up and down the streets like a demented horse, making the ground shake.

But when it came to the parson of the parish, Johannes was never in a good mood. He would appear in the man's bedroom, grab him and hold him in a bonecrushing hug. He tried to tear out the throat of the parson's wife, but her two daughters came to her rescue. It was said that he assumed the shape of a pig and attacked the parish-house cook. Then, for good measure, he pressed the lips of the parson's son together so firmly that the boy couldn't open his mouth.

No records tell us why Johannes had such a grudge against the parson. But the vampire seems to have spent a good deal of time making the poor man miserable. It was claimed that Johannes filled the parson's house with such a terrible smell that everyone there became sick. The parson himself developed inflamed eyes and almost went blind.

The stories about Johannes's doings grew wilder and wilder. People said he could change milk into blood. Farmers claimed that he pulled up their fence posts — posts it took two strong men to lift. He killed cows and dogs. He even tried to kidnap serving maids out of their beds.

One morning it was noticed that his gravestone had fallen over on one side, and the grave itself had several large holes in it through which the lid of his coffin could be seen. That was enough for the townsfolk. They dug him up, and found him looking much healthier than the day they had first buried him — six months before. When they punctured a vein in his leg, it bled.

Following tradition, a stake was pounded into the body. With a bellow of rage, Johannes opened his eyes, glared at them, and yanked the stake out.

Next they decided to burn the body. But first they tried to haul it out of the grave with thick ropes. The body suddenly became so heavy that the ropes broke. Then they tied more ropes to him and the ropes to strong dray horses. This time they got the body up and loaded it onto a cart. The horses, sweating and trembling, could hardly drag the cart.

It took 250 logs of wood to burn up Johannes. But finally the troublesome old man was reduced to ashes, which were carefully gathered up and tossed into the river. A vampire, it is said, cannot stand running water.

The remedy had worked before for the shoemaker of Breslav. It worked again in Pentsch. No one ever again complained of being bothered by old Johannes.

THE DARTMOOR TERROR

There are places in this world where it's all too easy to believe in ghosts. Dartmoor, a bleak plateau in southwestern England, is one of those places. Stretching 22 miles long and 20 miles wide, it is studded with rocky summits or *tors*, and made dangerous by small grass-covered bogs. It is said that some of these bogs have no bottom. There have been cases of visitors, caught by fog or darkness on Dartmoor, who have never been seen again.

But those treacherous bogs weren't the problem in the spring of 1918. Visitors and people who lived in the area were in danger — if they used the broad, modern highway that had just been built across 20 miles of desolate bogland.

The highway was the best that modern

engineering could construct. It had no blind corners or tricky curves. Yet an unusual number of accidents took place on it in 1918. And almost without exception, the victims reported that the accidents had been caused by something *invisible*!

The case of Bob Jeans was typical. Bob was a farmer's son who had borrowed his father's horse and carriage to take his girl for a drive. Although it was March, the evening was clear and mild. Bob and his sweetheart, Mercy Cotter, were jogging along in the carriage, talking over plans for their coming wedding. It was a leisurely ride because Mary, the old horse pulling them, could only manage a steady trot.

"Can't you make her go any faster?" Mercy asked. "My mother isn't feeling well, and I promised to be back before nine."

Bob shook his head. "Sorry. Mary's seen her best days. We'll be lucky if she doesn't drop in her tracks and leave us stranded out here."

"Don't say such things! They say the moor is haunted. Turn Mary around and let's start back."

"I was only joking," Bob said. "We've got plenty of time . . ."

He broke off as the reins were suddenly jerked from his hands. They were pulled upright into the air and held taut for a minute, then yanked back, pulling Mary's head sharply back. Then the reins flicked through the air to whip across the old mare's flanks. She reared and broke into a gallop. Mercy and Bob clung desperately as the carriage rattled and bounced along the road.

Suddenly the old horse halted, as if yanked to a stop. The carriage tilted, and went over. As he hit the ground, Bob felt a stinging blow to one side of his head — as if someone had struck him with a heavy fist.

Trembling, Bob and Mercy got to their feet and took a hasty inventory. No bones seemed to be broken, but that was the only good news. One wheel of the carriage was smashed. And poor old Mary, her jaws covered with blood-flecked foam, lay dead on the road.

Two hours later, Mercy and Bob stumbled into the Cotter house. They told of the unseen something that had snatched the reins and struck Bob. To their surprise, Mr. Cotter took their story seriously.

"We'll walk over to Dobbs' Inn tomorrow, Bob," he said. "There's a young fellow — an American army officer — staying there that I think you should talk to."

The next day, Bob and his father got to the inn shortly before noon. They found Lt. John Frost sitting in the small garden behind the inn. His leg, sheathed in a plaster cast, was propped up on a stool.

"Tell the lieutenant what happened to you last night, Son," Mr. Cotter prompted after he had introduced Bob.

Nervously, Bob repeated the story of his adventure on the Dartmoor road. As he did so, he wondered why he was telling it to a stranger, and whether the lieutenant would think he was crazy. "It sounds insane, I know," he stammered at the finish.

"Do you think so?" Lt. Frost asked. "I don't. Let me tell you how I broke my leg."

A week before, Lt. Frost had been given leave. He decided it would be restful to cross Dartmoor on his motorcycle. It was a trip he had done before, and one he looked forward to.

"I know Dartmoor quite well. And even though there's a lot of fog this time of year, I felt with the new road, I'd be safe. I've been across the moor on rough tracks, so I was looking forward to a smooth ride at top speed on a good road.

"Well, I was spinning along without a care in the world. No problems with the weather — it was cold but clear. When I got to that long straight stretch, I really opened the machine up. There was nothing in sight to stop me. I could see straight ahead to where the road begins to climb to that little hill about five miles beyond.

"The machine was handling perfectly, just swooping along, when something grabbed the handlebars. I could feel them being twisted out of my hands. Then I was all over the road, weaving wildly from one side to the other, fighting to control the motorcycle."

"That sounds like what happened to me!" Bob said.

"Yes, but it wasn't the worst of it," said the

lieutenant brusquely. "I *saw* hands . . . two huge hands wrapped around my wrists. There was nothing else, no arms, no body attached to them. Just the hands, gripping me like a vise. They were so big that they could hang onto me and still clamp down on the handlebars.

"They wrenched those handlebars around so that they were almost at right angles to the road. I remember flying through the air and coming down hard on the road. The cycle seemed to zoom through the air as if it had been shot from a cannon. I couldn't believe I hadn't been killed at first. But I can tell you that the experience might have given me a nervous breakdown if I hadn't found out from the police that I wasn't the first to meet the Phantom of Dartmoor."

He told Bob about two other cases he had learned of: a boy whose bicycle was lifted into the air as he rode it; a motorist who claimed invisible hands grabbed his steering wheel. "And that's probably only part of it. What about the increase in fatal accidents on that road? How do we know they weren't caused by the same thing that attacked us?" asked the lieutenant.

In April and May, more accidents happened. People who lived in the area avoided the road. It didn't seem to matter how you traveled it — by horse, wagon, bicycle, or car — those hands might come at you from out of nowhere and thrust you into disaster.

What was behind the haunting of Dartmoor

road? Some psychiatric experts said it was mass hysteria. Frightened people, expecting trouble, were probably accident-prone. But there was another theory. It was said that the hands belonged to a farmer who had hanged himself when part of his land was taken by the government so that the road could be built.

But in late May, a woman came to the police station. She was middle-aged and sensible-looking, but what she said wasn't sensible at all.

"No farmer ever had hands like those!" she told the constable on duty.

The constable asked her what she was talking about.

"Why, those hands that smashed the window of my car," she replied. "Yesterday evening, I was traveling along the Dartmoor road when my car just stopped dead. Now I'm pretty good with engines, but no matter what I did, I couldn't get it started again. Since it was getting dark, I decided to stay put and wait until daylight. So I locked the doors, closed the windows, and lay down on the back seat.

"I guess I fell asleep. The sun was coming up when the crash awoke me. A huge fist, like two of yours together, had smashed through the window. There was nothing attached to it — just a fist. I'll never forget what it looked like — big gnarled fingers, covered with hair, and long curved nails like claws. It grabbed the steering wheel. I was too frightened to scream. I rolled onto the floor and crawled out the other side. Then I ran."

A passing driver picked the woman up about 10 minutes later. She was running along the road and crying hysterically. He offered to go back to her car with her, but she refused.

" 'Just take me to the nearest police station,' I told him," she said. "He kept asking me what had happened. When I told him, he mentioned that story about the farmer who hanged himself. But that thing wasn't a ghost hand. It was heavy and solid, and terribly strong."

Later, she agreed to go back to her car with the constable. It was just where she said she had left it. Except for the smashed window, it was all in one piece.

"Everything else in place, Ma'am?" asked the constable.

She didn't answer. She just pointed — to the muddy but unmistakable print of a huge hand on the windshield.

The print was like a signature to a farewell note, because this was the last time anyone reported seeing the phantom hands. But the accident toll is still heavy on the beautiful, open road. Of course, cars are faster now than they were in 1918, and the traffic is heavier. If the Phantom of Dartmoor is still around, it can't honestly take all the credit for disasters that befall drivers on the Dartmoor road today.

LITTLE HAUNTED HOUSE ON THE PRAIRIE

The wheat fields of North Dakota in the late 19th century weren't the most exciting place on earth to live. Up until one summer morning in 1890, 12-year-old Rhetta Linner had thought there was no place duller.

Things started to become exciting when the Linners sat down to breakfast. Before the family's astonished eyes, fried eggs rose from the plates, sailed through the air, and spattered against the walls. Pancakes whizzed about like frisbees. Coffee cups did somersaults, scalding everyone in range. Then came a sound like that of rapidly moving scissor blades, and Rhetta's neatly cut long hair fell to the floor.

There was more excitement ahead. Mrs. Linner's best dress was found hanging from the barn loft and slashed to ribbons. The family dog was mysteriously sheared almost bald. Haystacks, neatly spaced in one field, were somehow moved overnight into another.

The Linners were at their wits' end. They knew that what they were facing wasn't normal — but *what* was it? Dan Prout, who had hired on to help with the harvest, thought he had the answer.

"What you folks have got is a *poltergeist*," said Dan. "My mother used to tell about them in the old country."

Poltergeists were something new to the Linners, but they are nothing new to most of the world. They have been defined as "noisy, mischievous ghosts or spirits." No one knows for certain what causes their manifestations, but there are many cases on record of their frightening pranks. Unlike most ghosts, they are never seen. But they are certainly heard. They throw furniture and crockery about, bang on doors, and have even been known to shake entire houses until the windows rattle. Small fires also sometimes break out where a poltergeist is busy.

As if the Linners didn't have enough to worry about, Dan Prout brought up another disturbing point. "Poltergeists get their energy from young people in the house. It seems to me that your girl Rhetta is just about the right age."

All eyes at once turned to Rhetta. Was she somehow causing all these things to happen?

90

"I haven't done anything!" Rhetta cried desperately. "None of this is my fault."

"I don't really see how it could be," Mrs. Linner agreed. "Rhetta has been with us every time something happened. She couldn't have moved those haystacks and then set them down without a straw out of place."

"What do you think you're saying, Prout?" growled Mr. Linner.

"I don't exactly know," Prout admitted. "But it's a proven fact that poltergeists fancy places where there's a young person around. I've heard tell they operate through young folks who have grudges. . . ."

"That will be enough of that, Prout," Mrs. Linner declared. "There's a natural explanation for all of this, I'm sure. I don't want any more talk about ghosts and such around here."

But Prout's words preyed upon Rhetta's mind. Was it somehow her fault all these awful things were happening. Did she have a secret grudge that was giving the poltergeist energy? She couldn't think of one. She could only remember feeling bored before all the disturbances.

In spite of Mrs. Linner's rebuke to Dan Prout, Rhetta noticed a new attitude on the part of her family. They watched her all the time. Either her mother or her father was always nearby. She became nervous and withdrawn, and prone to break dishes and upset things. "That was my fault," she would explain hastily when she dropped a plate, or accidentally turned over a basket of wet wash.

This miserable state of affairs was interrupted by the poltergeist itself. A shout from Mr. Linner brought the family to the barn one morning. Written in whitewash on the wall near the barn roof were the words: "RHETTA WANTS TO PLAY."

"That settles it for me," said Mrs. Linner. "There is no way this child could have gotten up there to write that."

"Doesn't seem likely," her husband agreed.

Rhetta felt a moment's relief. But something else was happening in the barn. The temperature seemed to have dropped, so that the hot summer day became chilly. Then stones began to fall from the dimness at the top of the barn.

Rhetta was an old woman when she told this story. But she had a very vivid memory of those stones. "They fell slowly, almost like leaves drifting down. They fell all around us, but none of them struck us. And when we picked them up, they were warm. I remember thinking that this spook, or whatever it was, really did want to play. It was showing off, like a mischievous child."

That night when Rhetta went to bed, the poltergeist stayed awake. Her covers were yanked off. When she got up and tucked them back on the bed, her pillow was thrown out the window. Then her clothes were yanked off their pegs and flung about the room.

"I started to cry. It just seemed like we had all been through so much, and maybe it would never end. Besides, no matter how it couldn't be proved, people would always think I had something to do with it."

How do you get rid of a poltergeist? Rhetta says her mother came up with the answer.

One evening a few days later, Rhetta and Mrs. Linner were together in the living room, mending workclothes. A peculiar trickling sound drew their attention. They listened for a minute, then decided it was coming from the kitchen.

When they investigated, they found a gallon jug of molasses overturned on the table. The molasses had been poured out from a height to form sticky letters on the floor. "RHETTA PLAY OR BE SORRY," they said.

Mrs. Linner's lips tightened. "We'll clean up this mess, and then we'll have a talk," she said.

"I don't know what I can say, Mama," Rhetta muttered.

"I don't mean you, dear. There's someone else here who needs talking to," Mrs. Linner replied.

When the kitchen had been put to rights, Mrs. Linner sat down and motioned Rhetta to do likewise. "Now," she said firmly, "Rhetta is not going to play with you — whatever you are. You are too badly behaved to play with anyone. From now on, no one in this family is going to pay the slightest attention to you, no matter what you do."

A large breadboard sailed into the air and crashed to the floor. Two cups spun off their hooks and shattered.

Mrs. Linner rose calmly. "Come, Rhetta. We still have some sewing to do."

"It took time, and it was no fun, but we stuck to our guns," Rhetta recalls. "For days afterward, there was all sorts of mischief. Mama's wool skeins were all found tied in knots. The sleeve of my Sunday dress was torn out and thrown in the well. There wasn't an unbroken dish left in the cupboard. Once or twice Papa started to lose his temper, but Mama would nudge him, and he'd pretend not to notice all the commotion going on.

"In about a week, things started to quiet down. I remember it was a Sunday morning when it all came to an end. I woke up early because I felt a hand touch my cheek. In a minute I felt it again. It was stroking and patting my face. A small hand, like a child's. I didn't see it, but I saw what it had written on the wall with chalk: 'RHETTA,' very wobbly and weak.

"I pretended I didn't notice anything, and closed my eyes. But my heart was beating very fast. Then I heard the piece of chalk snap as it hit the wall. For the first time I felt sorry for the poltergeist. It's terrible to be ignored. Every child knows that."

It may be terrible, but stern aloofness worked for the Linners. So if your household should ever be plagued by unexplained breakages and noises, try paying no attention to it. It — whatever it may be — just may get discouraged and go away.

THE MYSTERY
MOONS OF MARS

Is there life on Mars? Maybe — if you count vegetation. "If there's any communication on Mars, it's probably one lowly moss talking to another," says astronomer Harlow Shapley.

Was there ever life as we know it on Mars? Were there ever Martians? Maybe, says Russian physicist I. S. Shklovsky.

Dr. Shklovsky believes that Deimos and Phobos, Mars' two tiny moons, aren't moons at all. He suggests that they may be artificial satellites! According to his theory, Martians may have launched these satellites and used them as launching platforms for spaceships to carry them to more hospitable planets.

Here's why he thinks so. The Martian moons weren't discovered until 1878, although Mars had been under careful observation since the invention of the telescope. If the moons are really satellites, were they launched in 1878?

"No other planet has such tiny moons," says Dr. Shklovsky. It is estimated that Phobos may be 14 miles in diameter, and Deimos only eight miles. And it's not only their size that has Dr. Shklovsky wondering. It's the fact that they don't behave the way moons should.

Phobos is only 3,700 miles from Mars From the Martian surface, it would appear only about one-third as big as our moon does to us. And Phobos whirls around Mars every seven hours and 39 minutes — three times every Martian day. It is the only known moon in our solar system with an orbit shorter than the rotation period of its planet. It moves so fast that it seems to rise in the west and set in the east. As it rises, it appears as a crescent, but by the time it sets, it's a full moon.

Deimos is almost, but not quite, as freaky. It is 12,500 miles from Mars, and revolves around the red planet once every 30 hours (roughly the length of the Martian day). But since it's traveling almost at the same speed as Mars, Deimos keeps falling behind the turning surface. For this reason, it stays above the horizon for two-and-a-half Martian days at a time, while Phobos races past it.

Here's another one for Dr. Shklovsky. Both moons follow the equator of Mars, placed just as we place artificial satellites above the Earth. But if that coincidence doesn't impress you, how about this one? The Martian moons are not only tiny, but unusually light in weight. Dr. Shklovsky claims they are *too* light to be anything but hollow. He believes their light weight is the reason for their strange orbits, which are contracting, as if the moons were gradually "falling back" to the planet's surface. As Shklovsky points out, the Martian atmosphere is too thin to drag down a solid moon — but perhaps not too thin to pull on hollow spheres!

"The changes in the nature of the movement of Phobos are so great," says Shklovsky, "that, in just a mere 15 million years, Phobos will fall on Mars. Astronomically speaking, this is a relatively short period."

Changes in a moon's orbit might be caused by tides on its planet. But there are no tides on Mars. Some astronomers suggested Phobos is being affected by space dust. But they couldn't explain why space dust doesn't seem to be bothering Deimos.

"Phobos is hollow inside, something like a can from which the contents have been removed," concludes Dr. Shklovsky. "But can a natural cosmic body be hollow inside? No! Consequently, Phobos is of artificial design ... an artificial satellite of Mars!"

Needless to say, not every astronomer goes along with Dr. Shklovsky's idea of Martian satellites. The mystery got a new twist when Photograph No. 91 was taken 86,000 miles above Mars by Mariner 7.

It was a photo of Phobos. Instead of a glistening space station, it showed what seemed to be a lopsided potato-shaped chunk of rock. It measured 11 miles from pole to pole, and 14 miles in diameter at its equator. And it proved to be the darkest heavenly body ever seen in our solar system.

Astronomer Bradford A. Smith, a member of the Mariner scientific team, believes the photo proves Phobos is a rock that may have been captured by Mars' gravitational field after the planet was formed. There does seem to be a tremendous impact crater in the little moon's side, as if it might have been struck by a meteor while moving through space.

There was also a photo taken by Mariner 7 of Deimos. It turned out to be shaped like a sphere.

U.S. astronomers believe that those photographs go a long way toward proving the moons of Mars aren't space satellites made by Martians. But even so, suppose there were once Martians on Mars, and that they shipped out to escape their dying world. Where could they have gone?

Is it possible that they might have headed for our moon, seeking a temporary base? Some scientists believe that enough oxygen may be trapped in moon caverns to support life. And Martians would be accustomed to breathing very limited amounts of oxygen.

Whether or not the moon was the Martians' destination, lunar-watchers have reported strange goings-on for years. In 1783 and 1787, English astronomer Sir William Herschel reported seeing lights "like the torches of a procession" near the crater Plato. In 1950, astronomers Dr. James Bartlett, Jr. and Dr. Percy Wilkins both reported seeing an oval-shaped glow hovering over the floor of the Aristarchus crater. And in 1953, John O'Neill, then science editor of the *New York Herald Tribune*, claimed he had seen a gigantic bridge-like structure spanning the Mare Crisium.

O'Neill's observation was backed up by Dr. H. P. Wilkins, an authority on the moon, and by Irish lunar authority Patrick Moore. Although our astronauts have since landed on the moon, we still don't know what it was that these three trained observers really saw.

Is it possible that our own moon offers even more unsolved mysteries than the off-beat moons of Mars?

WHEN THE SKIES WENT BOOM

Every summer, vacationers flock to the wooded valleys and rolling hills of upstate New York. They bring with them plenty of excitement and noise. But when the summer is over and the vacationers are gone, the residents of this beautiful area expect to enjoy some peace and quiet. They didn't get much of either during November and December, 1977. Loud booming noises from the skies shook them awake at night, and startled them during the day.

The noises were like nothing people could remember hearing. One man described them as sounding "like an immense express train going 100 miles an hour overhead." Since there aren't any express trains in the sky, police looked for another explanation. Were the noises caused by aircraft? Explosives? Experts like Dr. William Donn of Columbia University checked out both possibilities, and said no.

On November 25, 1977, a New York farmer named Colledge was dropping off to sleep about midnight. Suddenly a tremendous booming noise came from overhead. It shook his house, rattling glassware and china.

Then a brilliant light lit up the window. "I jumped up and ran over to see what was happening," Colledge reported. "At first I thought something in the neighborhood had blown up. Then I saw *it*, hovering about 150 feet off the ground near the barn."

As Colledge describes it, the hovering object was shaped like an arrowhead. It seemed to be roughly 75 feet across and about 80 feet long. It also had red oscillating lights — "like the ones on a police car," plus bright white lights that bathed the area in brilliance. "It looked like it had four engines in the back," Colledge reported. "You could actually hear the atmosphere around it crackling from the tremendous noise they made."

Mrs. Colledge also saw the strange craft. From the bedroom window they watched It move slowly away, crossing the valley beyond. It disappeared behind a hill.

Three minutes later, and three miles away, a tremendous boom rocked the house of Bob and Margaret Travers. The Travers ran outdoors, followed by their 16-year-old son, Tom. All three got a good look at the UFO.

According to Bob Travers, "It was darned near as big as a house. It was shaped like an arrowhead, with red, green, and white lights. We saw two or three rows of square lighted areas on it, like windows."

Other residents of the area also heard the loud rumbling, booming sounds, and felt the heavy vibrations. Some called to ask if an earthquake had hit the region, but the instruments at the nearest geological observatory hadn't picked up any tremors.

The Travers called Hancock Air Force Base to see if any military or commercial aircraft were in the region. The base reported none at the time the UFO was sighted.

The experiences of the Travers and the Colledges were like an overture to the biggest sound-and-light show of the century. At 9:25, 10 days later, a loud mysterious rumble shook up the East Coast of the U.S. from New Jersey to North Carolina. This time the jolting booms were picked up by sensors at the Lamont-Doherty Observatory. The needle on the instruments jumped right off the paper.

Right after the loud reverberating noises came those shuddering vibrations, strong enough to make buildings tremble and windows and walls crack. At the Oyster Creek Nuclear Plant in New Jersey, the shaking was so long that officials thought it was an earthquake, and evacuated all the employees.

Along with the sound effects, reports began to come in about light flashes and fireballs. And, as you might expect, reports of UFO sightings increased. One UFO believer tried to explain the connection by stating, "When a UFO enters our atmosphere, it makes a noise like 100 sonic booms." But he couldn't explain why UFOs only seemed to be bugging the East Coast lately.

Mrs. Phyllis Crowell of Elysburg, Pennsylvania, says the noises had a definite UFO connection. On December 5, 1977, she was driving her daughter home from school. Suddenly a loud reverberating sound shook the ground, forcing Mrs. Crowell to stop the car. As she did so, the road was bathed in a brilliant white light.

"I stuck my head out of the window," she recalls. "Moving slowly across the road, about 200 feet up, was a UFO. I won't ever forget what it looked like. It had bright white lights in front, and a bright blue light in back. Then all at once it split in two. The blue-lit part zoomed off in one direction, and the white-lit part in another."

In the days that followed, the noises continued along the East Coast. Sometimes the shocks they produced activated smoke detectors in houses. Now the noises were being heard as far south as Florida.

The New Year of 1978 also started off with a bang and more booms. From January 3rd until January 6th, the people of North and

South Carolina got their heaviest bombardment. Then things quieted down.

But folks who had to live along the East Coast raised some noise of their own. They demanded to know what had caused the booming, the earth tremors, and the weird flashes of light. The White House ordered top government agencies to investigate the mystery.

The Defense Department, the Coast Guard, NASA, the Interior Department, and the National Oceanic and Atmospheric Administration investigated. Their verdict: "We have no explanation for any of the reported explosions off the East Coast."

"They can't be explained," the Geological Survey stated flatly.

But what about these possible explanations?

Sonic Booms. No way. The booms and blasts were far too powerful to be made by any known aircraft.

Secret Military Experiment. "If it's some kind of secret weapon, it's not ours," said a Pentagon spokesman. But Drayton Cooper, a TV reporter in Charleston, South Carolina, blames secret testing of military weapons plus supersonic flights from the Marine Corps air station at Beaufort, South Carolina. "The booms in our area all began after 8:00 A.M., and were never heard on weekends. Military planes don't ordinarily fly off the base on weekends." But the base officials said they weren't doing anything to cause the booms.

Earthquake Activity. Scientists at Columbia University and the University of South Carolina say the reverberations showed up on their machine like earthquake tremors — but earthquakes weren't causing them.

Exploding Gas. A New Jersey scientist suggested that bubbles of methane gas might be causing the booms. He said the gas might be rising from garbage dumped at sea by New York and New Jersey. This idea doesn't explain the shaking and light flashes.

Dr. James Devine, head of earthquake studies at the U.S. Geological Survey, says the booms are nothing new. "Muffled booms accompanied by flashes of light have been heard for hundreds of years in many parts of the world. In the past they have been reported from the Middle East, Australia, the Midwest, and New England. New England settlers called them the 'Guns of the Senecas.' Loud mysterious booms were reported in connection with earthquakes in 1795 in Boston, and in 1775 in New Jersey. In 1888, the booming noises, light flashes, and ground tremors shook up the East Coast for several months."

Perhaps the most original explanation came from Charles Fort, a New York newspaperman. In the 1920's, he began to collect news clippings of odd happenings. He found plenty of clippings telling of explosions in the sky, accompanied by strange lights and earthshaking. He also found that not only noises came out of the sky. Sometimes, along with the booms, came "rains" of weird objects — live fish and frogs, hot stones, red soot, burnt clumps of hair, and even pieces of cooked flesh!

This got Fort to thinking. He said that we on Earth "live at the bottom of an ocean of air," and perhaps interplanetary navies fought battles above us in the sky. According to him, the shaking and noises might be the sound and vibration of these battles. And the strange "rains" might be the wreckage of star ships.

We may never know the real reason for the mystery booms. But since history has a way of repeating itself, we can be pretty sure that they haven't stopped for good. Someday the skies over your neighborhood, and the ground under it, may vibrate to loud, unexplained noises. It's happened before and it will probably happen again. When it does, will anybody have the true explanation?